New Holland Honeyeaters, *Phylidonyris novaehollandiae* (see page 50).

Australian
BIRDS

Long-billed Corella, *Cacatua tenuirostris* (see page 34).

Photography by Ken Stepnell
&
Text by Jane Dalby

NATIONAL
BOOK DISTRIBUTORS AND PUBLISHERS

Ken Stepnell, renowned as one of Australia's leading photographers of our natural wonders, travels over 100 000 kilometres annually continually searching for new subjects to enhance his superb photographic library.

His eye for detail has enabled readers to appreciate the beauty and variety of our natural resources through many publications. His photographs show the delicate balance of nature and the need to preserve our heritage.

Jane Dalby was encouraged to take an interest in natural history by her parents and grandparents. She obtained a B.A. in Biology and Ecology from Macquarie University. She is now a Technical Officer at the National Herbarium at the Botanic Gardens, Sydney, New South Wales. This involves looking after the collection of dried plants used in research and identification.

Her great interest in birds has developed over the last four or five years and has led to an extensive study of their habits and features.

Apart from bird-watching, pottery fills her leisure hours.

Black Swans, *Cygnus atratus* (see page 25).

Published by
National Book Distributors and Publishers
3/2 Aquatic Drive, Frenchs Forest, NSW 2086
First published 1986
Reprinted 1987, 1988, 1989 (twice), 1991, 1993, 1994, 1996
Photography © Ken Stepnell 1986
Text © Jane Dalby 1986
Typeset in Australia by Deblaere Typesetting Pty Ltd
Printed in Singapore by Kyodo Printing Co (S'pore) Pte Ltd

National Library of Australia
Cataloguing-in-Publication data

1st ed.
Includes index.
ISBN 1 875580 41 7.

1. Birds—Australia. 2. Birds—Australia—Pictorial works.
I. Dalby, Jane, 1945– . II. Title.

598.2994

BIRDS AND THE ENVIRONMENT

The fossil record shows that birds have been present in Australia for at least 130 million years and it is now thought that the ancestral stocks of Australian birds come from two sources. A number of families seem to have originated in the southern super-continent, Gondwanaland, having evolved from ancestors present when the Australian continent began drifting northwards, about 100 million years ago. Emus, mound-building birds, frogmouths and parrots belong in this category.

Later, as the Australian continent approached Asia, during the last 15-20 million years, birds from the north were able to colonise Australia by island-hopping. New species then evolved in the isolation of the Australian continent. The recent arrival and establishment in Australia of the Cattle Egret and the Sarus Crane, a close relative of the Brolga, demonstrate how Asiatic birds are able to colonise this continent. Conversely, birds from families which have evolved here, e.g. honeyeaters, have colonised islands to our north and in the Pacific, evolving new species there.

Today, there are about 8800 species of birds in the world, and of these, approximately 700 can be seen in Australia. About 570 are resident breeding species, while the others are either regular or occasional non-breeding visitors. To appreciate how these birds are able to occupy Australia, we need to know something of the diversity of habitats available for them to use.

Australian Pelicans, *Pelecanus conspicillatus* (see page 21).

The Australian Environment

Superb Blue Wren, *Malurus cyaneus* (see page 46).

Climate
The island continent of Australia extends over 33 degrees of latitude and covers an area roughly equivalent to one third that of North America. Consequently, the climate varies widely. Generally speaking, the north has wet summers and dry winters, while in the south, the reverse applies. On the east coast, the weather pattern is more complicated, as it is affected year-round by rain depressions from the Pacific and the influence of the Great Dividing Range. Most of Australia experiences hot summers, while winters are generally cool rather than cold. Frosts are common in southern and inland areas, and snow often falls in the highlands of the southeastern mainland and Tasmania.

Topography
There are few high mountains in Australia to present significant barriers to the movement and distribution of such mobile animals as birds. Most of the continent is comparatively flat, while the majority of the mountains extend along the east coast, in a broad belt from Cape York to Tasmania, with some isolated peaks in the arid centre and the northwest of Western Australia. The only alpine areas are in the southeastern ranges.

Rainfall
Except for Antarctica, Australia is the world's driest continent, with over 30 percent of its area receiving less than 25 cm of rain per year. With the exception of the Murray-Darling river system in southeastern Australia, rivers are few and relatively short. The rain that falls in the interior often flows towards the centre of the continent, ending up in swamps or in ephemeral lakes, many of which are saline. These areas may remain dry for long periods. Above-average rainfall, often in far-distant catchments, may lead to flooding which is slow to subside and consequently has long-lasting effects.

The Habitats
The vegetation occurring in a particular area is determined by a combination of soil, topography and climate. Most of Australia's vegetation is evergreen and is notable for the dominance of two genera of trees and shrubs – the *Eucalypts* and *Acacias*. In most cases, a number of different plant species occur together, their different flowering and fruiting times producing a variety of food for birds and other animals. However, the suitability of a particular habitat for a particular species is determined not only by the availability of food and water, but also by such needs as nesting and roosting sites and other specialised requirements.

There is great variation between habitats in the number and diversity of birds which are able to be supported. The habitats, which often intergrade and intersperse with one another, range from the desert and arid grasslands of the interior to the floristically rich rainforests of northeastern Queensland.

In the following pages, the major habitat types are described, giving examples of the birds to be found there. Wherever possible, the species illustrated are mentioned where they are typical of a particular habitat.

Rainforests

Rainforests have a patchy distribution in high rainfall areas along the east coast and highlands from Cape York to Tasmania. They may conveniently be divided into three main types, from tropical in the north, through subtropical, to temperate in the south.

Tropical rainforests are the most complex of all environments, having the greatest number of plant species, with the trees often reaching more than 30 metres in height. There are two or three tree layers with the crowns of the tallest trees forming a closed canopy. Palms and lianas are common, and the ground cover usually consists of mosses and ferns. The many distinctive birds to be found in tropical rainforests include the Cassowary, Scrub Turkey, fruit pigeons and bower birds.

In subtropical rainforests, there are usually two tree layers, with fewer species of trees and lianas than in tropical rainforests, but with more mosses and epiphytic ferns. One tree species may become dominant over a large area, e.g. Coachwood, *Ceratopetalum apetalum*. Scrub Turkeys, Golden Whistlers, whip birds and scrub wrens are all typical of these forests.

Temperate rainforests are often dominated by one tree species, e.g. Antarctic Beech, *Nothofagus cunninghamii*, with many ferns and tree ferns, epiphytic mosses and lichens. These forests are less diverse than the other types and also cover a smaller area, so they are able to support fewer species of birds. The Scaly Thrush and Yellow Robin are two birds of temperate rainforests.

Sclerophyll Forest

The term sclerophyll refers to plants with stiff, hard leaves. It is applied to forests of medium to tall trees, dominated by eucalypts, many species of which have hard, leathery leaves. These forests occur down the east coast of Australia, from Mackay in Queensland to Victoria and southern South Australia, as well as in Tasmania and the southwest of Western Australia. Their composition is largely determined by rainfall and to a lesser extent, by soil fertility.

Wet sclerophyll forests, which are dominated by one or more eucalypt species, are found in areas where rainfall is over 100 cm per year. The trees are usually over 30 metres tall, and the forest canopy is usually closed. There is an understorey of shrubs or tree ferns, and a deep layer of accumulated litter on the ground. King Parrots, flycatchers, the Yellow Robin and the Rufous Bristle Bird are some of the species to be found in wet sclerophyll forests.

Dry sclerophyll forest occurs in areas of moderate (75-100 cm) annual rainfall. These forests, which are characteristic of poorer soils, are usually dominated by two or more species of eucalypt. The trees are generally less than 30 metres tall, with the canopy either open or closed. The understorey is composed of drought-tolerant shrubs, and there is usually not a deep litter layer. The birds typically found in these habitats include thornbills, the Spotted Pardalote and the Scarlet Robin.

Most birds supported by sclerophyll forests are, at least partly, insect-eaters, and, compared to other habitat types,

Temperate rainforest on the path to Russell Falls in the Mount Field National Park in Tasmania. Tree ferns, other ferns and epiphytic mosses and lichens are common in the understorey.

there are few seed-eaters. A number of species, including honeyeaters and lorikeets, are attracted to the blossom which is characteristic of these forests, and which provides a supply of nectar, pollen and insects for these and other birds.

Woodlands

Woodlands include a range of habitats, from tree-dotted grasslands to open types of forest.

Tropical and subtropical woodlands occur in a wide band across the north of the continent. Eucalypts predominate, with several different species occurring together. Various combinations of tall perennial grasses, herbaceous plants and annual grasses comprise the understorey.

Temperate woodlands occur in the southwest of Western Australia and in a strip from southern Queensland to the southeast of South Australia. The dominant trees are usually several species of eucalypt, sometimes associated with species of Native Pines, *Callitris*, and Belah, *Casuarina*. In southwestern woodlands, the understorey is dominated by shrubs, while in the southeast, there is a continuous short ground cover of annual and perennial grasses and herbs. Grey Fantails, rosellas and thornbills are characteristic birds of these areas.

Semi-arid woodlands occur on flat or undulating country, in areas receiving between 35 and 75 cm of rainfall annually. They extend from the Kimberleys in northwestern Australia, across the north, and down eastern Australia west of the Dividing Range, to southwestern New South Wales. Apart

Salmon Gums, *Eucalyptus salmonophloia*, dominate the woodlands along the Eyre Highway between Balladonia and Norseman in Western Australia. The low understorey is composed mainly of Bluebush, *Maireana* spp.

from various eucalypts, a number of other tree species may be dominant, e.g. Boree (*Acacia* spp.), Bean Tree (*Lysiphyllum cunninghamii*) and Tea Tree (*Melaleuca viridiflora*). The understorey usually has one or more shrub layers, as well as a ground cover of grasses and herbaceous plants. The Mallee Ringneck, Red-capped Robin, Red-rumped Parrot and the Golden Whistler are some of the species which frequent these woodlands.

In arid woodlands, the trees are rarely taller than eight metres. In the north, the dominant trees may be species of *Eucalyptus*, *Acacia* or *Lysiphyllum*, while in the south they may belong to other genera, such as *Casuarina* or *Callitris*. Species characteristic of arid woodlands include the Mulga Parrot, woodswallows, babblers and the Yellow Robin.

Woodlands support almost three times as many bird species as rainforests or sclerophyll forests, which are floristically the richest habitats. About 40 percent of these species are specialists, which depend to a great extent on woodlands for all their needs. Insect-eaters, in particular, use both forests and woodlands, while migratory and nomadic birds move throughout the eastern belt of these two habitats.

Scrublands

Scrublands are dense communities composed of low trees, often with a closed canopy. They fall into two main types, the dominant tree genera being either *Eucalyptus* or *Acacia*.

Mallee is a scrub of small, multi-stemmed eucalypts, usually with at least two species being dominant. The understorey is composed of a variety of shrubs and perennial grasses. Short-lived grasses and herbs appear after rains. Mallee occurs in semi-arid areas across southern Australia, from the vicinity of Griffith in New South Wales, through northwestern Victoria and the south of South Australia, to the south-west of Western Australia. The best-known and widespread acacia scrubs are those dominated by Mulga, *Acacia aneura*, Gidgee, *A. cambagei* and Brigalow, *A. harpophylla*.

Woodswallows, White-browed Babblers and Yellow-plumed Honeyeaters are all typical scrubland birds. The most characteristic is the specialist mound-building bird, the Mallee Fowl.

Grasslands

Native grassland communities are usually treeless and range from the alpine grasslands occurring in the southeastern highlands through to the extensive Mitchell Grass (*Astrebla* spp.) plains and Spinifex (*Triodia* spp.) communities of arid and semi-arid areas. In the tropics, swampy grasslands occur in coastal areas while tropical grasslands are to be found inland from the Gulf of Carpentaria.

In addition, large areas of grassland have been created by the clearing of forests and woodland for grazing of cattle and sheep, e.g. in the Riverina area of New South Wales.

Many birds which feed in grassland use adjacent scrub or woodland for roosting and nesting. Typical grassland birds include the Cockateil, Crested Pigeon, various species of finch, the Bustard, and the Spur-winged Plover.

Arid zone

Several habitat types occur in the arid zone. Saltbush, *Atriplex* spp., and Bluebush, *Maireana* spp., plains occur in the southeastern inland, where the rainfall is between 15 and 50 cm per year. Well-spaced low shrubs dominate, with ephemeral grasses and herbs appearing after rain. The Orange Chat is typical of these areas. The arid Mitchell Grass plains are treeless and are found in the Northern Territory and Western Queensland, where summer rains fall. Spinifex grassland occurs, often with scattered trees and shrubs, on sand dunes and rocky and stony country in the centre and northwest of Australia.

True desert, where the rainfall is less than 20 cm per year, is relatively uncommon. 'Gibber' or stony desert, is covered with small rocks and broken stone, and may be without any vegetation at all, or may have occasional small sparse plants. The Gibber Bird or Desert Chat, is one of the birds typical of these habitats.

In sandy desert, both the dunes and the zone between dunes may be vegetated or without any plant cover. Dune vegetation is usually a spinifex community, while between the dunes, low trees, shrubs and grasses may grow. After rains, many ephemeral plants appear. All these arid habitats may occur separately in large areas, or may be interspersed with other habitat types.

Usually only drought-adapted birds stay in these areas during dry periods, although large populations may be supported during good seasons. After suitable rains, nomadic species such as woodswallows, finches, various parrots, the Emu, Bustards, and chats move in to exploit the abundant but short-lived food supplies.

Heaths

Heaths are communities found on infertile soils and are composed mainly of low shrubs. They occur in tropical and wet subtropical coastal lowlands, the southeastern alpine region and in dry areas in the temperate southeast and southwest of the continent.

Coastal heaths have rich, diverse floras, which provide food in the form of seed, nectar, pollen and insects. They may support large numbers of birds, although not a great diversity of species. The Scarlet Robin, Tawny-crowned Honeyeater and the New Holland Honeyeater are all typical of heathlands. Alpine heaths support few birds, especially in winter.

Termite mounds in arid open woodland in the Northern Territory. Hooded Parrots, *Psephotus dissimilis*, nest in these mounds, laying their eggs in a chamber excavated at the end of a short tunnel.

Stony desert in the Pilbara region of Western Australia. Few birds are able to survive year-round in these arid habitats, although after rains nomadic species may move in to exploit short-lived food resources.

11

Wetlands

Wetlands occur where land is permanently or temporarily flooded with fresh, brackish or salt water. They include habitats ranging from the bare mud flats and shallow waters of estuaries to permanent and ephemeral lakes and swamps and man-made water storages. The vegetation varies greatly, from sparsely vegetated sand flats to a variety of plant communities dominated by samphire, aquatic plants, grasses and sedges, heath plants and shrubs, or trees such as mangroves or red gums.

Apart from coastal or estuarine habitats, the wetlands of Australia may be divided into four regions based on rainfall patterns and river systems – the arid centre, the Murray-Darling river system, the northern tropical region and the southern temperate zone.

In the central arid region, the headwaters of the rivers are in areas of low and unpredictable rainfall. Occasionally, extensive flooding covers large areas, filling swamps and water holes for periods which are usually no longer than a few months. In response to the changed conditions, nomadic water birds such as pelicans, cormorants, ibis and egrets

Black Swans, *Cygnus atratus*, with their family of cygnets on Bool Lagoon in South Australia. Permanent swamps are important habitats for many bird species, especially in times of drought.

move in large numbers into the now-favourable areas to breed. As the water recedes and the food supplies diminish, the area is abandoned until suitable conditions again prevail, perhaps years later.

The Murray-Darling wetlands support many of Australia's water birds, including ducks, cormorants, spoonbills, ibis, egrets and swans. The permanent swamps of the Riverina in particular, provide a very important refuge in times of drought.

In the tropical region, which stretches across northern Australia and down the east coast to northern New South Wales, there are two distinct seasons, known as 'The Wet' and 'The Dry'. The first rains usually begin in October, with the heavy monsoon rains falling between December and March. In the early part of the dry season, the swamps and lagoons recede but their margins continue to provide green feed and grass seed. The Brolga and the Magpie Goose are two well-known birds of this region.

Southern temperate wetlands are found in coastal areas from northern New South Wales to the southeast of South Australia, and in the southwest of the continent. They are permanent, being filled by winter rains and summer storms. Australian Shelduck and Chestnut Teal are characteristic of these wetlands, while Black Swans are particularly common. Coastal wetlands are also important drought refuges for inland birds.

Coastal Habitats

Mangrove communities, though restricted in area, are important to many birds, with at least 35 species of land bird being characteristic of them. The mangrove flowers attract nectar and insect-eating birds from adjacent areas. Ibis, herons, and egrets also use mangroves as sites for nesting colonies.

Estuaries, where fresh and salt waters meet, are inhabited by many species of water bird, such as pelicans, cormorants and gulls. The mud and sand flats are of particular importance to the migratory wading birds which arrive from their northern hemisphere breeding grounds in spring and return north in autumn.

Apart from mangrove and estuarine habitats, coasts provide diverse environments such as rocks and beaches, cliffs and offshore islands.

Ground-nesting sea birds such as the Little Penguin, shearwaters, pelicans and terns are just a few of the birds which use these islands for breeding.

Altered Environments

All habitats are influenced, either directly or indirectly, by human activities. Forests and woodlands have been lost by clearing for grazing and agriculture, while as a direct result, the area of grassland has been increased. Pasture improvement has altered natural grasslands and over-grazing has degraded many habitats, particularly those in the arid and semi-arid zones where erosion is a serious problem.

Wetlands are being lost by filling and draining, changed by dam building and by the use of the waters for irrigation. Degradation by dumping of rubbish and toxic wastes still occurs, while salting has become a problem in some irrigated areas.

Feral mammals, such as foxes and cats, impose increased predation pressure on native animals, while introduced birds compete with native species for food and nest sites. Major habitat damage is caused by hoofed animals, particularly in fragile ecosystems such as arid lands and wetlands.

Habitat destruction has especially serious consequences for specialised birds such as the Mallee Fowl, which cannot survive once suitable habitat has gone. Such activities as clear-felling of forests also result indirectly in the death of birds. They simply have nowhere to go, as all the territories in the adjoining areas are already occupied. Illegal robbing of nests by egg collectors and the removal of chicks from nests, as well as trapping of birds for the avicultural trade, pose a serious threat to the survival of birds which may already be

Pelicans, *Pelecanus conspicillatus*, may be seen on large areas of shallow water in coastal or inland areas of Australia. The enormous bill with its soft pouch is used in catching food.

rare. This applies especially to parrots, finches and birds of prey.

For some species, man-made changes may be beneficial. For example, many birds and mammals are able to exploit new water resources supplied by bores, farm dams and large water storages. Clearing of woodland and forest has provided ideal conditions for such birds as the Peewee, which prefers open habitats. Agriculture has provided increased food supplies for seed-eaters such as Galahs, Sulphur-crested Cockatoos and Corellas, and fruit-eaters such as King Parrots and rosellas. Because of the conflict this causes with farmers who suffer damage to their crops, some species have been considered agricultural pests. For birds of prey, such as the Wedge-tailed Eagle, the introduced rabbit has come to be a large component of its diet. In spite of the evidence of the beneficial effects of this, these birds have long suffered persecution, particularly in grazing areas, because of their unjustified reputation as major predators of lambs.

The Birds

Over millions of years birds have evolved numerous features which fit them for life in the many different environments available to them. Among the most notable of these are the adaptations which make flight possible.

Structure

The skeleton is very light, the bones being very thin or hollow, reinforced with internal struts where extra strength is required. Teeth have been lost and replaced by the light, strong bill.

The fusion of the pelvic bones has given strength and rigidity, with the resulting loss of movement being compensated for by the development of a long, flexible neck.

The powerful muscles necessary for flight are anchored to a flat projection of the breastbone, the keel. Where the ability to fly has been lost, as in the Emu, the flight muscles and wings have been reduced, and the keel on the breastbone has been lost.

The flexible wings, which have evolved from the forelimbs, are shaped to reduce drag and provide lift. Propulsion is provided by the primary feathers, which also act as flight controls, in conjunction with the feathers of the tail. The streamlined body shape has a smooth surface, provided by the contour feathers.

Wings have evolved in different ways appropriate to different types of flight. For example, the long, thin wings of

Long-billed Corella, *Cacatua tenuirostis* (see page 34).
Fairy Penguin, *Edyptula minor* (see page 19).

albatrosses and shearwaters permit sustained, low-level gliding without the need to beat the wings. Soaring birds such as the Wedge-tailed Eagle have long, broad wings which provide great lift and allow them to circle slowly on thermals. The wings of hovering birds such as the Kestrel, and the humming birds of the Americas, rotate at the shoulder, producing a down-draught and maintaining the bird in a stationary position.

To sustain flight, birds require large amounts of energy, and must therefore spend a large part of their time feeding. They also need a very efficient respiratory system. To achieve this, the lungs are augmented by at least nine interconnected thin-walled sacs, which lie in the body cavity. These sacs not only carry large quantities of oxygen to the tissues, but also help to disperse the heat generated by the strenuous muscular activity needed for flight.

Feathers

One feature by which birds can be distinguished from all other animals is the possession of feathers. Extremely strong and light, feathers are made of keratin, as are the scales of reptiles and the hair and claws of mammals. The plumage not only contributes to flight and streamlining, but also functions in other ways, which include provision of waterproofing and insulation against heat and cold.

Contour feathers each have a central shaft, which in turn has a hundred or more filaments on each side. The filaments of flight feathers bear minute barbs which, by hooking on to each other, produce a continuous surface to allow the feather to push against the air. Soft fringes on the flight feathers of night-hunting birds, such as the Tawny Frogmouth and the Barn Owl, act as mufflers on the wings to allow silent flight.

Below the contour feathers are fine hair-like filo plumes, as well as down feathers, which trap an insulating layer of air against the skin. Some birds, including herons, parrots and woodswallows, possess powder down. These feathers fray constantly to a fine powder, which is used in grooming and gives the plumage of these birds a characteristic bloom.

Penguins, which have lost the ability to fly and have adapted for a life in the sea, have a thick, even coat of filamentous feathers. By trapping a layer of air next to the skin, these feathers provide insulation, and prevent penetration of water. Another flightless bird, the Emu, also has filamentous feathers, which have no barbules, as they no longer have the need of flight feathers.

Grooming

It is essential for a bird's well-being that its plumage be kept in perfect condition. Consequently, grooming, which is carried out by scratching with the feet and preening using the bill, takes up a large part of each day.

Most birds dress the feathers with an oil which is secreted by a gland on the rump, at the base of the tail. The contour feathers are carefully preened and repositioned, while each flight feather is drawn through the bill, ensuring that the barbules are 'zipped' together, maintaining the continuous surface of the feather.

In addition to preening, many birds sunbathe, or ruffle their plumage in dust or water. They may even deliberately allow insects such as ants to crawl amongst the feathers.

Mutual grooming or allopreening, which is practised by many birds, serves the dual purpose of strengthening pair-bonds while grooming the plumage in areas which are hard for the individual birds to reach.

The feathers of cormorants are less waterproof than those of other birds. When the birds dive, the feathers become wet, thus reducing buoyancy. However, this means that they must dry their plumage once they have finished fishing. To do this, they perch in a convenient place with their wings out-stretched, until they are dry and the feathers can be preened.

All birds need to renew all their feathers each year. Most lose them in a predetermined pattern, the moult progressing slowly over the whole body. However, a few birds, such as penguins, do not do this, but lose all their feathers at once. Since penguins cannot fly, they are not put at such disadvantage by this as birds which need to be able to fly to escape pre-ators. Other birds such as Black Swans, shelducks and other waterfowl, moult all their flight feathers at once, just after the breeding season. As a result, they become flightless until the new feathers grow. At this time, they tend to congregate in large numbers on lakes, where they are not so vulnerable to predators.

Colour and Camouflage

Feathers appear coloured because they contain pigment, because the structure of the feather reflects light of a particular wave length, or because of a combination of the two. In some species, the bill, or the skin of the legs, feet, head or neck may be brightly coloured. For example, the Purple Swamphen has a red bill, facial shield and legs, while the breeding male Brush Turkey not only has red skin on the whole of the head and neck, but also has a bright yellow wat-tle around the lower neck.

Conspicuous colouring aids the recognition of species and sex, particularly in combination with displays and song. In some cases, such as the Red-capped Robin, the Superb Blue Wren and the Chestnut Teal, the male is brightly coloured, while the female is much less conspicuous. Gregarious birds may use colour to keep the flock together.

Cryptic colouring and shading combine to make a bird inconspicuous, as with the Black Duck and the Bush Stone Curlew. The camouflaging effect of cryptic colouring may be enhanced by the behaviour of a bird such as the Tawny Frog-mouth, which during the day assumes an upright posture so that it resembles a dead branch. Chicks and eggs of ground-nesting birds such as the Bustard and the Silver Gull almost always have camouflage colouring.

Movement

Birds move about in many ways other than by flying. Con-sequently they have evolved feet suited to many purposes, including running, perching, swimming and grasping.

Perching birds have developed a mechanism in their feet, whereby the toes automatically lock when the bird alights on to a perch. Similarly, the talons of a striking bird of prey, such as a falcon or an owl, close automatically as the legs bend on impact with the prey.

Movement over the ground may be by hopping, walking or running. Emus, as with other ratites, have lost the power of flight. They have evolved long, powerful legs and relatively small three-toed feet, so that they have the ability to run very fast when necessary.

Some birds such as parrots are able to use one foot as a 'hand', by standing on one leg, whilst holding an object up to the bill with the other foot.

Treecreepers have large feet with long toes and sharp claws, to help them grip the bark of trees as they move in a spiral up the trunk, searching for insects.

The mound-building birds such as the Scrub Turkey and the Mallee Fowl have strong legs and feet which they use in building the mound which is used for incubation of the eggs, and for scratching for food in the soil and leaf litter.

Swimming birds like ducks, swans, cormorants and peli-cans have webbed feet, while others such as grebes have lobed toes. In addition, their legs are set well back in the body, to assist in swimming. However, this also has the effect of making them ungainly on land. This is particularly marked in grebes, the legs of which are situated almost at the tail.

Penguins, having abandoned flight, have adapted to life in the sea, and have evolved webbed feet. When they swim, their flippers, which are the wings modified for swimming, are used for propulsion, while the feet act as rudders. Because the flippers are used in a flying motion for swimming, the large flight muscles and keeled breastbone have been retained.

Feeding

The evolution of numerous bird species, able to exploit the many food sources available, has been accompanied by the development of a great diversity of beaks.

Beaks consist of two bony mandibles covered with a layer of keratin, which is replaced as it wears. They usually open by movement of the lower mandible, although in some groups of birds, the upper mandible is hinged and capable of considerable movement. The strong bills of cockatoos and other parrots, for example, are hinged top and bottom, giving extra leverage for cracking nuts and woody fruits.

The bill-tips of some birds have touch receptors which en-able them to locate unseen prey. Ibis, for example, probe with their sensitive sickle-shaped bills in soft ground or mud, while spoonbills sieve small organisms from the water using their flat bills in a sweeping motion. Touch receptors are also to be found on the palate and tip of the tongue, so that the bird is able to feel what it has in its bill. The tongue may be used to manipulate food, cockatoos for example feed using the muscular tongue in conjunction with the bill and the foot.

Nectar-feeding species such as lorikeets and honeyeaters have evolved brush-tipped tongues adapted for collecting nectar. This feature has also developed in some species which do not feed primarily on nectar, e.g. woodswallows and the Mistletoe Bird.

Because birds lack teeth and cannot break up food by chewing, this function is performed by the muscular gizzard.

Mistletoe Bird, *Dicaeum hirundaceum* (see page 53).

Food items small enough are usually swallowed whole, though birds of prey and other strong-billed birds are able to break or tear food up before they eat it.

Seed eaters such as pigeons and finches have a sac in the throat, the crop, which is used to store food. This allows them to feed quickly and move to a place where the food can be digested in greater safety.

The Mistletoe Bird, which feeds mainly on mistletoe berries, has developed a specialised digestive system to deal with this diet. The gut is a uniform tube, through which the berries pass quickly, the fleshy outer layer being digested and the sticky seeds voided, often on to a branch. Here they may germinate and grow into a new plant, thus ensuring a future food supply for the bird.

Foraging

Birds use many feeding methods, and this often enables similar species to coexist in the same habitat. Several different species of thornbill often travel in mixed feeding flocks, each species foraging in a different part of the vegetation. For example, the Brown Thornbill feeds in the upper foliage, while the Yellow-rumped Thornbill stays in low vegetation and on the ground.

In wetlands, waders with different bill and leg lengths probe the mud to different depths. Others chase small organisms on the surface of the water or mud. Some ducks dabble for food on the surface of the water, while others up-end in shallow water. Yet others, such as the Musk Duck, dive for prey on the bottom. Black Swans, with their long necks, feed in deeper water, where they can reach plants growing on the bottom.

Insect-eaters have many different ways of feeding. The robins watch from a perch and pounce on their prey in the leaf litter. Flycatchers also hunt from a perch, but catch their insects on the wing. Swallows do all their hunting in the air, either flying quite high up, or skimming over the ground. These birds even drink on the wing.

Communication

Birds communicate largely via a combination of visual and vocal signals. Colour and pattern combine to convey information about the species and sex of a bird. Where the sexes are alike in appearance, song and display identify the sexes. Special feathers such as the erectile crests of cockatoos and the breeding plumes of birds such as herons and egrets act as signals conveying information about them to other birds. Each species has a number of characteristic calls, each used for a different purpose. Territorial calls, which are loud and directional are used to proclaim ownership of territory as well as to attract a mate. In some species, the male and female call in duet. The male Whipbird, for instance, makes the first part of the well-known whipcrack call, and the female completes it.

Alarm calls are also loud, but non-directional, warning other birds in the vicinity of danger, without revealing the position of the caller. Birds of other species also recognize and react to these calls.

Flocks, groups or pairs feeding in dense cover keep together by making quiet contact calls. Other flock birds such as lorikeets, when feeding in forests, keep in contact using both their brilliant colours and their loud, shrill calls.

The calls of young birds, combined with the characteristic colour and pattern of their gaping mouths, act as stimuli to the adult birds to feed them. Young cuckoos have a call to which the adults of other species respond by feeding them. In this way, the chances of survival of young birds are increased.

Outside the breeding season, some birds may be found alone. Others live in family parties, e.g. Kookaburras and Superb Blue Wrens, or small flocks, e.g. Red-rumped Parrots. Other species such as Galahs and Little Ravens spend most of their lives in flocks.

Groups and flocks often have a social arrangement where one bird is dominant over all the others. In the pecking order, each bird has its place, being subordinate to some and dominant over other members of the flock. The sexes may each have a separate hierarchy.

Courtship and Breeding

Courtship displays reduce the usual aggression between individuals, so that mating can take place. They also help to synchronise the birds physiologically for breeding. This is important for pairs of birds, and in some species, for whole colonies. Courtship varies widely between species, from the dancing displays of the Brolga and the bowing and cooing of pigeons to the presentation of a gift, in the form of a fish, by the male Fairy Tern to his mate. This process not only culminates in mating, but establishes a pair-bond which ensures cooperation between the two birds in rearing the young.

Long-lived species such as Wedge-tailed Eagles, which mate for life, go through prolonged and elaborate courtship when they first pair up, but in subsequent breeding seasons may mate with a minimum of display.

In some species, such as bower birds, males mate with several females, each of which builds a nest and rears the brood alone. Female Emus take no part in the care of their eggs and young, and may either remain with the male, or leave. The male incubates the eggs and rears the young, caring for them for up to 18 months. As a result, male Emus may breed only every second year.

To breed successfully, all species need suitable nest sites, as well as a plentiful supply of food to support themselves as well as the young. Newly-independent birds need abundant food supplies to compensate for their lack of experience.

In Australia, the occurrence of suitable breeding conditions may vary from year to year and from place to place. In temperate areas, most species breed after the winter rains, when the weather is becoming warmer and insects are abundant.

In the tropics, the monsoon rains are the dominant influence. Water birds breed at the end of The Wet, while birds of the forest and grasslands breed in the dry spring. Many species, particularly those of the arid inland, have the ability to breed at any time of year, providing conditions are right.

Nests and Young

There is great variation in nest types, from the scrape in the ground used by such birds as terns, to the enormous nests of sticks built by Wedge-tailed Eagles and added to over the years. Flycatchers and robins make beautifully neat nests of plant fibre matted with spiderweb and lined with soft-materials, while pigeons and doves lay their eggs on a flimsy platform of sticks. Peewees and swallows build using a mixture of mud and dry grass, shearwaters and Little Penguins use a shallow burrow in the ground, while many species of parrot need a tree hole or hollow limb.

Cuckoos do not build a nest at all, or even rear their own young. They are nest parasites, the female laying an egg in the nest of another species. On hatching, the young cuckoo throws the chicks and eggs of the host out of the nest, and it alone is reared by the unsuspecting foster parents.

The Scrub Turkey and other mound-building birds lay their eggs in a mound of soil mixed with decomposing vegetation, the heat from which does the job of incubation. The mound is tended by the male, who is able to monitor the temperature of the soil by testing it with his tongue, and to regulate the temperature by removing or adding material.

Young Mallee Fowl and Scrub Turkeys are completely independent from the time they hatch and dig themselves unaided from the nest mound. They are able to fly and to feed themselves from the first day. Chicks of other ground-nesting species, such as ducks, swans, Emus and others, have a covering of down when they hatch and are able to walk or swim with their parents very soon after hatching. In most species, however, the chicks are blind, naked and helpless when they hatch, and require a long period of incubation and care by their parents before they are able to leave the nest.

Incubating mound of the Mallee Fowl, *Leipoa ocellata* (see page 31).

Little Corellas, *Cacatua sanguinea*, gather around a water trough and windmill in the Flinders Ranges, South Australia. Provision of permanent water, especially in dry habitats, allows many birds and other animals to survive in areas which would otherwise be unsuitable.

Migrants and Nomads

Migrants make regular, twice-yearly movements of all or part of the population from one area to another, and may move within Australia or undertake immense journeys to and from the northern hemisphere. From overseas, migration to Australia is limited to a few species, most of which are the wading birds which breed in the northern hemisphere and spend the northern winter here. Shearwaters, on the other hand, breed on islands in southeastern Australia and migrate to the north Pacific each year after breeding. Young birds do not return to the nesting colonies until they are five or six years old and ready to breed.

Some Australian species undergo a yearly migration within Australia, mostly in the eastern belt of forest and woodlands, or move from Australia to New Guinea, travelling north in autumn and south in spring. However, not all the population takes part in these migrations, with some birds remaining behind for the winter. The Sacred Kingfisher, Yellow-faced and White-naped Honeyeaters and the Welcome Swallow are just some of the species which undertake these migrations.

About a quarter of Australian bird species are nomads, wandering for most of the year, breeding where and when conditions are suitable, or wandering for a large part of the year and returning to traditional breeding sites. Ducks and other waterfowl, woodswallows, Diamond Doves and Mistletoe Birds are just some of the birds which are at least partly nomadic.

Bird-watching

The photographs on the following pages demonstrate beautifully something of the loveliness and diversity of Australian birds. However, there is no substitute for experiencing the beauty and interesting behaviour of birds by going out into the bush and observing them for yourself. A surprising number of species are to be found in suburban gardens and even city parks. Native birds may be attracted to your own garden by growing native plants which provide shelter, food and nest sites. A bird bath or feeder would also be attractive to the local birds, but they should be well out of the reach of cats.

All the equipment you will need to study birds is a pair of binoculars and a good field guide, so that you can identify what you see. Ideally you would also have the company of someone who knows birds and their ways, and is willing to share with you his or her knowledge and delight in them.

18

Shearwaters are so-called because of their characteristic flight pattern. They cover great distances gliding on long narrow wings, rising and falling close to the surface of the sea. Short-tailed Shearwaters, *Puffinus tenuirostris*, nest in great numbers in southeastern Australia, on islands and a few parts of the mainland. In the non-breeding season, they migrate to the North Pacific, up past Japan and return via the west coast of America. They feed on plankton.

Evening parade at Phillip Island, Victoria, as Fairy Penguins, *Edyptula minor*, return to their burrows after spending time at sea, fishing for themselves and their chicks. Although clumsy on land, they are superbly adapted to life in the sea, with streamlined shape and thick waterproof plumage. They 'fly' underwater using their flippers, which are actually modified wings, while their webbed feet and small tail act as rudders.

Fairy Penguins are the smallest of the world's penguins and the only ones to breed in Australia. They build a nest in a chamber at the end of a short burrow where they usually lay two white eggs. The adults take turns incubating the eggs and going to sea to fish. The bird illustrated is moulting from its downy juvenile plumage into adult plumage before leaving the burrow.

19

White-faced Storm-petrels, *Pelagodroma marina*, are usually seen in summer out at sea beyond the continental shelf off southern Australia. These small, long-legged petrels feed by day on plankton at the surface of the sea, returning at night to breeding colonies on coastal islands. They are thought to migrate to the north Indian Ocean in the non-breeding season.

Silver Gulls, *Larus novaehollandiae*, are a familiar sight to most Australians, as they can be seen, not only on beaches, but also far inland wherever suitable conditions occur. These birds are omniverous scavengers and have profited from man's activities such as farming and the easy food supply provided by our rubbish dumps. Unlike the adults shown here, with their immaculate grey and white plumage and red bills and legs, young Silver Gulls have dark bills and legs and mottled feathers.

Like many ground-nesting birds, Silver Gulls nest in colonies on offshore islands. The mottled eggs are laid in a shallow nest made in low vegetation. Incubation of the eggs and care of the chicks are shared by the parents.

Fairy Terns, *Sterna nereis*, are also known as sea swallows. They are to be found from about Derby in Western Australia along the western and southern coasts of mainland Australia and around Tasmania. In common with other terns, these graceful birds have fine, sharp bills, long narrow wings and forked tails. They forage for food by flying over the water, head down, plunging in periodically after prey such as small fish.

Fairy Terns nest in small colonies on islands and sandy coastal inlets. During courtship, the male brings the female an offering such as a small fish. If the gift is accepted, the pair then choose a nesting territory which they defend. Here, 1 or 2 well-camouflaged eggs are laid in a shallow depression in the sand.

Throughout Australia, wherever suitable shallow stretches of water occur, Australian Pelicans, *Pelecanus conspicillatus*, may be found. Large birds, with a wing span of 2.5 metres, they are accomplished flyers. They are also well adapted for swimming, having large webbed feet and legs set well apart and to the rear of the body. However, this arrangement means that, although they are good swimmers, they are awkward on land.

Pelicans can often be seen fishing cooperatively. A group of birds will swim together, in a tight circle, driving fish into shallow water, then all lunging with their large bills into the school of fish. The Pelican's bill, with its pouch of soft skin, is not only used in fishing. In hot weather the birds cool themselves by opening their bills and fluttering the skin rapidly.

Pelicans usually nest on treeless islands, in very large numbers, on inland waters or on the coast. Two or three eggs are laid in the nest, which starts as a scrape in the ground and is lined gradually with sticks and grass. After the young hatch, they need care from their parents for about 14 weeks.

The Little Pied Cormorant, *Phalacrocorax melanoleucos*, is common throughout Australia and Tasmania, on coasts and in inland water and even such small areas as farm dams and roadside ditches. Cormorants swim low in the water, diving frequently to catch small animals such as crustaceans, frogs and aquatic insects.

Because their plumage easily becomes wet, Cormorants must dry their feathers, which is why they are often seen perched with their wings outstretched, on such convenient places as jetties, beacons, rocks or branches. Nesting takes place in colonies, 2 to 5 white eggs being laid in shallow stick nests built in trees or bushes overhanging water.

White-faced Herons, *Ardea novaehollandiae*, occur over much of Australia as well as in eastern Indonesia, New Guinea and New Zealand. These lovely birds can be seen anywhere there is shallow water. Usually alone or in pairs, they hunt for small aquatic animals, or for insects such as grasshoppers. In the breeding season, adults grow long plumes on the back and long feathers called 'hackles' on the lower neck.

The Pacific or White-necked Heron, *Ardea pacifica*, which stands about one metre tall, may be seen usually alone or in loose groups, in shallow freshwater or wet paddocks. They are easily distinguished in flight by their large size and the two white patches on the bend of the wing. They nest alone or in small colonies, 3 or 4 blue-green eggs being laid in a loosely-built nest of sticks, in a living tree overhanging water.

The Great Egret, *Egretta alba*, is almost as large as the Pacific Heron. Although large numbers may occur at times, these egrets are usually seen alone or in small groups, in river shallows, flood waters, mud flats, swamps and other wetlands. In the breeding season, the appearance of these birds alters slightly, with the bill turning black and the skin of the face becoming green, with beautiful plumes growing on the wings.

The White Ibis, *Threskiornis aethiopica*, which is also known as the Sacred Ibis, ranges from Australia to Africa. It is very similar to the bird depicted in ancient Egyptian paintings, in which the god of learning, Thoth, is represented in the form of an Ibis. In Australia, the White Ibis can be found feeding in pastures and around the muddy verges of dams and lakes, while avoiding the more saline wetlands.

The Straw-necked Ibis, *Threskiornis spinicollis*, uses a wider range of environments than the White Ibis. Flocks are often attracted to dry paddocks by outbreaks of insects such as locusts. Adult birds have a black head and bill, yellow straw-like breast plumes, and glossy black wings and back. Two or three species of Ibis may breed together, in permanent wetlands or inland swamps which contain water only occasionally. Straw-necked Ibis do not nest in trees, but build a shallow nest of sticks and reeds above water, in thick cumbungi, reeds or lignum. The bills of young Ibis are short and straight, only developing the distinctive sickle shape as the birds mature.

White Ibis feed on small aquatic animals which they find by touch, probing in soft soil and mud with their long curved bills. They breed in mixed colonies with herons and spoonbills. The nests are platforms of sticks, built in trees over water or in trampled swamp vegetation.

West Australians have adopted the Black Swan, *Cygnus atratus*, as their State emblem. Swans favour expanses of water, ranging from fresh to salt, where aquatic plants are plentiful. When swimmimg or at rest, their plumage often appears to be all black, but they have white flight feathers which show up well when they fly. Black Swans usually feed in water, using their long necks to reach underwater vegetation. They also feed on floating water plants by dabbling.

The nest is a large mound of plant material placed in shallow water or on a small island. Between four and seven pale green eggs are laid and incubated in turns by the parents. After about 44 days, the eggs hatch over a period of two days. The young cygnets are covered with pale grey down. After breeding, the adult swans moult and temporarily become flightless.

The Royal Spoonbill, *Platalea regia*, is one of two spoonbills found in Australia. They frequent fresh and saltwater wetlands and inter-tidal swamps. They feed as they wade along in shallow water, sweeping their long flat bills to and fro. Small aquatic animals are located unseen, by the sensitive bill-tip. In breeding plumage, Royal Spoonbills have long white crests of snowy white plumes.

25

The Cape Barren Goose, *Cereopsis novaehollandiae*, is widely distributed on islands from the Recherche Archipelago in Western Australia to the islands off Wilsons Promontory in Victoria to the Furneaux Islands northeast of Tasmania. Flocks visit the mainland coast in summer. The geese breed in winter on islands, laying 3 to 6 eggs in a nest on the ground. The young stay in the nest territory for about six weeks, then join a crèche of young birds.

The Australian Shelduck, *Tadorna tadornoides*, is a handsome, brightly coloured duck which frequents shorelines of brackish lakes in the southeast and southwest of the continent. Females of this species have a chestnut breast with white around the eye and at the base of the bill. They have a high-pitched call. Males have a white neck-ring and their call is a low-pitched honk. Australian Shelducks nest in trees, sometimes choosing a hollow, which may be as much as 20 metres off the ground. After the young are hatched, the ducklings are led by their mother overland to the male's territory at the water's edge. Adults moult after the young are fledged, becoming flightless for a time.

The male Chestnut Teal, *Anas castanea*, is a handsome bird, having a glossy green head, bright chestnut breast and a white patch on the flank. The female, which is a mottled grey-brown, is easily confused with Grey Teal, which are generally paler and have a distinctly light-coloured throat. The sexes call quite differently, with the female giving a quack while the male's call is a whistle. Chestnut Teal are generally coastal birds, common on coastal waters from North West Cape in Western Australia to northern New South Wales.

Musk Ducks, *Biziura lobata*, belong to the group of diving ducks with stiff pointed tail feathers. Their common name comes from the musky smell of the males in the breeding season. They inhabit permanent swamps and lakes with dense vegetation as well as coastal swamps and inlets and occasionally the sea. The males, which have a large black lobe of leathery skin hanging below the bill, give a spectacular breeding display with tail spread and bill raised.

The Black Duck, *Anas superciliosa*, is a dabbling duck, easily recognisable by its light-coloured face with a dark stripe through the eye. It is found throughout Australia on all kinds of water, but prefers swamps with permanent water and dense vegetation. Its numbers vary from pairs to large flocks. Breeding occurs when conditions are suitable e.g. extensive areas of water and plentiful vegetation for food. The nest may be built on the ground, in swamp vegetation or in a shallow tree hollow. Eight to ten eggs are laid.

27

Grebes are sharp-billed diving birds which have lobed, rather than webbed toes. They often escape danger by diving rather than flying. Great Crested Grebes, *Podiceps cristatus*, inhabit swamps, lakes and streams. They are seen in pairs in the breeding season and in flocks at other times. Breeding pairs in characteristic breeding plumage give striking mating displays, appearing to run across the water. The nest is a mass of water weed built on a small island or a floating platform of weed anchored to a submerged object.

Hoary-headed Grebes, *Poliocephalus poliocephalus*, are so-named because of the grey, hair-like feathers which appear on the side of the head in the breeding season. These are lost in winter. They are frequently seen in flocks on swamps, lakes and brackish or salt water. The striped young of Grebes are able to swim as soon as they are hatched and are often carried on the adults' backs, even when they dive.

The Purple Swamphen, *Porphyrio porphyrio*, is a large, distinctive bird, with a bright red bill and facial shield, long reddish legs and feet and dark blue plumage on the head and body. It inhabits swamps and marshy areas, living and roosting in dense vegetation over water. When walking or swimming the Swamphen flicks its tail, showing white plumage under the tail. The nest is built on trampled reeds or cumbungi.

A small relative of the Swamphen, the Eurasian Coot, *Fulica atra*, is slate-grey with a darker head, a white bill and facial shield. They are common in a wide range of wetlands from fresh to brackish, in pairs or large flocks. The stone-coloured eggs, finely spotted with black, are laid in a nest built of swamp vegetation, in shallow water or on a low island.

Pied Stilts, *Himantopus himantopus*, are widely distributed throughout the world. In Australia they can be seen over almost all the country, in freshwater swamps and other wetlands as well as mud flats and estuaries. Adult birds have a white head and body with black nape and wings. The eyes are red and the legs a deep pink. Their call is a distinctive 'yapping'.

Young Pied Stilts have a grey crown and nape and dark legs. These slender, long-legged waders feed in water, often with the head submerged, or on dry ground. Food is also taken from the surface of the water. They nest in loose colonies on dry ground or on hummocks in the water. Four blotched stone-coloured eggs are laid and incubated by both parents.

All over Australia, wherever there are muddy or gravelly margins of rivers, lakes, dams or brackish marsh, the Black-fronted Dotterel, *Charadrius melanops*, is likely to occur. Usually alone or in pairs, these small native waders are distinctively marked, with a black band across the forehead and through the eye and a black 'Y' on the breast. The eye ring is red and the bill is red with a black tip. The three eggs, which are protectively stone-coloured with dark marbling, are laid in a scrape in the ground.

The Masked Lapwing or Spur-winged Plover, *Vanellus miles*, is well known for its distinctive appearance and strident call, as well as for its habit of diving on intruders who approach the nest too closely. The sexes are similar, with large facial wattles and a yellow spur at the shoulder. The well-camouflaged eggs are laid in a shallow nest built on open ground. Within a few hours of hatching, the young birds are able to run and feed themselves.

A Brolga's nest is built on a mound of grass and other vegetation raised above water level or on a small island in a swamp. Two spotted and blotched eggs are laid. Very soon after hatching, the young birds are able to run and swim. They are cared for by both parents.

The Banded Lapwing or Plover, *Vanellus tricolor*, is quite colourful, with its yellow bill and facial skin and red wattles. It is nomadic, usually to be found in drier open grasslands and plains, and prefers areas with little cover. The nest is a sparsely lined scrape in the ground. The adult birds will dive on any intruder in their nesting territory. If this fails, they will feign injury in a 'broken wing act'.

The tall and stately Brolga, *Grus rubicundus*, one of two cranes living in Australia, is probably known to many people for its group dancing displays. Accompanied by loud, trumpeting calls, pairs and groups of birds dance, bowing and leaping with wings spread and heads thrown back. As a result of swamp drainage and shooting, Brolgas are now uncommon in southeastern Australia and can be seen in numbers only in wetlands and flooded areas in northern and central Australia.

The Mallee Fowl, *Leipoa ocellata*, has adapted to the harsh environment of arid inland scrub and mallee in southeastern Australia. Mallee Fowl belong to the family of birds called 'mound-builders', which bury their eggs in a mound of soil mixed with decaying vegetation. The combined heat of the sun and decomposing organic matter provides the necessary warmth to incubate the eggs.

During the summer breeding season, between 16 and 33 eggs are laid in the mound at the rate of about one per week. When the female is ready to lay, the male digs a hole in the mound and the female lays the egg in the organic matter at the centre. The male tests the temperature with his tongue and maintains it at 33 °C by adding or removing material. The chicks hatch after about seven weeks and dig their way out of the soil unaided. They are independent straightaway, being able to fly within the first day.

The Superb Lyrebird, *Menura novaehollandiae*, is to be found in temperate and subtropical rainforests, woodlands and fern gullies in Eastern Australia from the Dandenong Ranges in Victoria to the south-eastern border ranges of Queensland. During the winter breeding season, the male sings and displays on a special mound built on the forest floor. Several females may mate with him, rearing the young alone in breeding territories nearby.

Lyrebirds are famous for their ability to mimic sounds such as bird song or even the sound of a chainsaw, incorporating them in their own characteristic song.

The Brush Turkey, *Alectura lathami*, another mound-building bird, lives in rainforest and wet open forests on the east coast of Australia, as far south as the Manning River. The 12 to 16 eggs are laid at intervals of a few days in the mound, which is about four metres in diameter and one to two metres high. It is built of leaves and other plant material, mixed with earth. The male regulates the mound temperature at about 35 °C.

Australian Bustards, *Ardeotis australis*, are ground-dwelling birds of open grasslands and grassy woodlands. Males gather in a 'lek', or display ground, where they attract females by displaying a fanned tail and drooped wings. With roaring calls, they spread their neck feathers until they reach the ground. Formerly widespread throughout suitable habitat, Bustards now occur commonly only in northern and central Australia, their range reduced by shooting, foxes and habitat destruction.

'Weeloo' is another name commonly given to the Bush Stone Curlew, *Burhinus magnirostris*, whose eerie, mournful call is a well-known night sound of the Australian bush. Singly or in pairs, these shy, yellow-eyed birds are usually most active at night. They live in open woodlands, timber along watercourses and scrub near beaches.

Emus, *Dromaius novaehollandiae*, lay a clutch of about nine dark green eggs in a scrape in the ground, lined with dry grass and other vegetation. The male incubates the eggs alone and acompanies the young birds for up to 18 months. The striped camouflage colouring of the young chicks disappears as they grow and learn to fend for themselves. The female may remain with the male and chicks or may leave and mate with another male.

The Australian coat of arms is supported by two of the best-known of Australian animals, the Kangaroo, *Macropus rufus*, and the Emu, *Dromaius novaehollandiae*. Australia's largest birds, standing up to two metres tall, Emus are flightless. They have tiny wings, but their legs are long and powerful, enabling them to run at speeds of up to 50 km per hour. In some regions they undertake long migrations. They eat fruits, seeds and other vegetable matter, as well as insects such as grasshoppers.

Galahs, *Cacatua roseicapilla*, are one of the most numerous and widespread of Australian parrots. They have been favoured since European settlement, by the growing of cereal crops, clearing of trees and provision of water and have expanded their range into the interior, coast and highlands.

Galahs do not breed until they are at least four years of age. Pairs mate for life and usually use the same nest-site each year, lining the hollow with fresh eucalypt leaves. About eight weeks after they hatch the young birds join a crèche, away from the nest tree, with other fledglings. They become independent after a further five weeks.

Long-billed Corellas, *Cacatua tenuirostris*, have a limited distribution from the southeast of South Australia, to southern Victoria and the southwest of New South Wales. These cockatoos usually frequent grasslands and paddocks close to timbered watercourses. They are rare birds but may be locally common where food is plentiful.

Long-billed Corellas eat fruits and seeds of grasses and other plants. Their elongated bills are used for digging up bulbs and roots. Their nest hollows are usually high in living trees near water. Between July and November, two or three eggs are laid in the unlined hollow.

Perhaps the most famous of our cockatoos, with the possible exception of the galah, is the Sulphur-crested Cockatoo, *Cacatua galerita*. It is a handsome white bird with a pale yellow crest and a voice that is a raucous screech. In pairs, small parties and sometimes in flocks of several thousand, they frequent a wide variety of timbered habitats, trees near watercourses, and parks and gardens. They feed on seeds, grain, fruits, blossom, roots and insects. They have, along with galahs, become serious agricultural pests in some wheat and oilseed-growing areas.

Only one small Australian parrot has a crest, the Cockateil or Quarrion, *Nymphicus hollandicus*. The male has a yellow crest, face and forehead and an orange cheek-spot, while the female is less brightly coloured and has a barred grey and yellow tail. They are widely distributed throughout the interior of Australia, inhabiting most types of open country close to water. Cockateils are well known to many people as they make delightful and affectionate pets.

35

Rainbow Lorikeets, *Trichoglossus haemadotus*, and Scaly-breasted Lorikeets, *T. chlorolepidotus*, are noisy, fast-flying parrots which live in forests, feeding on blossoms and fruit. Like other lorikeets, they have brush-like tongues adapted for gathering nectar and pollen. Hundreds of these birds are a major tourist attraction at Currumbin in Queensland, where they come down to be fed.

The brilliantly-coloured King Parrot, *Alisterus scapularis*, inhabits forest and open woodland along the east coast of Australia. Usually in small groups, they feed, both on the ground and in trees, on seeds, fruits, berries, nectar and leaf buds. The males have a scarlet head and body and dark green wings which have a pale green band. Females and young birds are mostly dark green with a red belly.

Within its range in eastern inland Australia, the Mallee Ringneck, *Barnardius barnardi*, is quite common in its preferred habitat of mallee, semi-arid woodland and *Acacia* scrubland. In pairs or small parties, they feed on the ground or in the outer branches of trees. Five eggs are laid in a hollow limb or tree hole and incubated by the female. The young leave the nest five weeks after hatching and remain with the parents for some time.

Moist forests from sea level to the mountains in the east and southeast of the mainland are the favoured habitat of Crimson Rosellas, *Platycercus elegans*. In the nest hole in a tree the 5 to 8 eggs are laid on a layer of decayed wood. Once independent, a few weeks after leaving the nest, young birds join flocks of immature birds. Predominantly green at first, they acquire increasing amounts of red feathers until full adult plumage is reached at 16 months of age.

The brightly coloured Eastern Rosella, *Platycercus eximius*, occurs in woodlands, open forest, farmlands, parks and gardens in southeastern Australia and Tasmania. They feed in trees or on the ground, eating seeds and fruits of a wide range of shrubs and trees as well as blossom, nectar and insects. A clutch of 4 to 9 eggs is laid in wood dust in a hollow tree or log. Young birds stay with their parents for about four weeks, after which flocks of independent young birds begin to form.

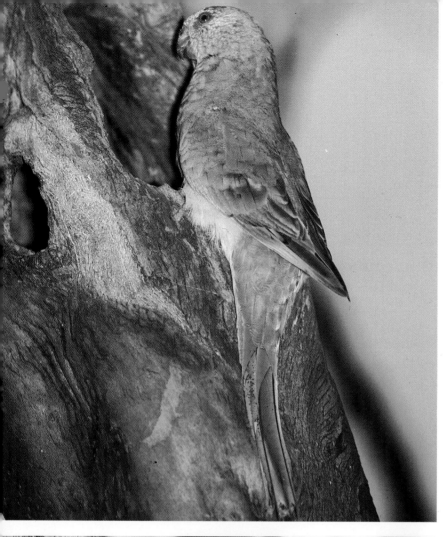

Throughout southeastern Australia, Red-rumped Parrots, *Psephotus haematonotus*, are found in pairs or small groups. In winter they appear in flocks, in open woodlands, mallee, farmlands and trees near water. They feed on the ground, mostly on seeds of grasses and herbaceous plants.

The female is duller in colour than the male, and has no red on the rump. The nest is in a tree hole or hollow limb, usually near water. The female broods the eggs for 19 days, being fed frequently by the male. About four weeks after hatching, the chicks leave the nest and, with the adults, join a feeding flock.

Usually seen in pairs or small groups, Mulga Parrots, *Psephotus varius*, occur in the southern interior of Australia, in arid shrublands, mallee and lightly treed grasslands, often near water. The male is more brightly coloured than the female, which has red instead of yellow on the shoulder and does not have red on the belly and thighs. After the young birds leave the nest, about four weeks after hatching, they remain in the family with the parents.

Blue-winged Parrots, *Neophema chrysostoma*, occur in a wide range of habitats, from coastal heaths and dunes, saltmarsh, grassland, mallee and saltbush to alpine areas over 1200 metres. They breed in Tasmania, the coast of southern Victoria and southeastern South Australia. In winter, partial migration takes some birds as far north as southern Queensland. The female is slightly paler in colour than the male.

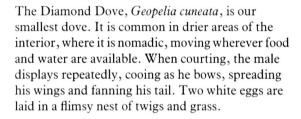

The Diamond Dove, *Geopelia cuneata*, is our smallest dove. It is common in drier areas of the interior, where it is nomadic, moving wherever food and water are available. When courting, the male displays repeatedly, cooing as he bows, spreading his wings and fanning his tail. Two white eggs are laid in a flimsy nest of twigs and grass.

Crested Pigeons, *Ocyphaps lophotes*, are usually to be seen in groups of five or six, in lightly wooded grasslands near water. They feed on the ground on seeds and some insects, spending the rest of the time in shrubs and trees. In flight, their wings make a distinctive whistling sound. The frail nest is built of a few twigs in dense cover, in a bush, tree or stump.

The Common Bronzewing, *Phaps chalcoptera*, is found in wooded habitats, except rainforest and wet sclerophyll forest, throughout Australia including Tasmania. The most widespread of Australian pigeons, it is wary and hard to approach. It is seen usually alone or in pairs, feeding on the ground in or at the edge of scrub. The twig nest is built in a variety of sites from the ground to bushes or tree branches. Two eggs are laid.

A nest of mud pellets, reinforced with grass or straw and lined with grass, feathers and hair is built by Welcome Swallows, *Hirundo neoxena*. The cup-shaped nests, like the bottle-shaped nests of Fairy Martins, are built on vertical surfaces on riverbanks or cave walls, or under man-made structures such as bridges and the eaves of buildings. Skilled and graceful flyers, they drink and feed on the wing, catching large numbers of small flying insects.

The Rainbow Bee-eater, *Merops ornatus*, is aptly named for its glowing colours. However, although bees and wasps form part of its diet, all types of flying insects are taken on the wing, including moths, dragonflies, beetles and grasshoppers. Bee-eaters migrate to New Guinea and the surrounding islands in autumn, returning to southern Australia to breed in spring. The nest is built in a chamber at the end of a burrow dug in a sandy bank.

Australian red-breasted robins were originally so-named by people homesick for the similarly-coloured English robin. The male Scarlet Robin, *Petroica multicolor*, is recognised by its white forehead, white slash on the wing and tail, and scarlet breast. The female, which also has a white forehead, has a pale red wash on the breast.

Scarlet Robins are widespread in suitable habitats in southeast and southwest Australia. They breed in woodlands and forests, moving in autumn and winter to more open habitats. The female builds the cup-shaped nest and incubates three eggs, during which time she is fed by the male. Both parents tend the young birds.

A male Red-capped Robin, *Petroica goodenovii*, easily recognisable with his red cap and breast, is pictured here feeding his mate on the nest. The small neat nest is well camouflaged in the fork of a tree. Red-capped Robins watch for prey while perched on a low branch or stump, taking food on the ground and also on the wing. They live in drier parts of the country in scrub and woodlands.

White's Thrush, *Zoothera dauma*, is Australia's only native thrush, occurring in wet forests in eastern Australia and Tasmania as well as in Southeast Asia and southern Europe. The Scaly Thrush, as it is also called, is a ground-feeder in thick undergrowth and can be difficult to see, protected by its colouring and by its habit of freezing when approached. Two or three speckled greenish eggs are laid in the bowl-shaped nest in a vertical tree-fork.

41

The Eastern Yellow Robin, *Eopsaltria australis*, is typical of shaded habitats in wet open forests, woodland and coastal thickets in eastern and southeastern Australia. Quiet but not shy, Yellow Robins will sit on a low perch watching for prey, pouncing suddenly and returning to the same or a new position. The young birds are brown with pale streaks and attain adult plumage a few weeks after leaving the nest.

A female Hooded Robin, *Melanodryas cucullata*, perched on the side of the nest while the male stands by. This species is usually found in pairs, in dry forests, open woodland, mallee and scrublands throughout mainland Australia, except for Cape York Peninsula. Hooded Robins hunt by sitting motionless on a prominent perch and pouncing on insects on the ground.

The bright black, white and yellow plumage of the male Golden Whistler, *Pachycephala pectoralis*, is in strong contrast to the well-camouflaged colouring of the female. Young males take 3 to 4 years to develop the brilliant adult plumage. These whistlers inhabit rainforest, open forest, woodland, mallee and coastal vegetation in eastern and southern Australia from Cairns to Geraldton.

Rufous Whistlers, *Pachycephala rufiventris*, occur throughout Australia, being common in open forest, woodland, mallee and arid scrub. They are present but less common in wetter tall forests.

Male and female Rufous Whistlers are very different in appearance. The female (above) is brownish-grey above and buff with dark streaks below, while the male (right) has a dark head and back, with a black band separating the white throat from the rufous underparts. Both Rufous and Golden Whistlers are known by the name 'Thunderbird' because the males of both species respond to a sudden noise such as a crack of thunder by bursting into song.

The Satin Flycatcher, *Myiagra cyanoleuca*, is aptly named, the male being glossy black with white underparts. The female is blue-grey above with a white belly and a chestnut throat and breast. The nest, which is usually built on a horizontal dead branch, is a small cup made of strips of bark and moss, matted with spider web.

Satin Flycatchers feed by darting into the air for flying prey. They breed in southeastern mainland Australia and Tasmania, arriving in spring and leaving in autumn. Most migrate to New Guinea for the winter, although some remain in north Queensland.

A Grey Shrike-thrush, *Colluricincla harmonica*, brings a lizard to feed its young. These birds feed on a variety of small animals including other birds and nestlings. They live in forest, woodland and scrubs all over Australia, from the coasts to the dry inland. Because of their melodious call, heard especially in the breeding season, they are also known as Harmonious Thrush.

Rufous Fantails, *Rhipidura rufifrons*, build a wine-glass shaped nest of bark and grass, bound with cobweb, in a fork in a thin branch. They are birds of rainforests and thick scrubs, on the eastern and northern coasts of Australia. In winter, Rufous Fantails migrate to north Queensland and New Guinea, returning to the southeast to breed.

Common in forested and woodland habitats throughout Australia, Grey Fantails, *Rhipidura fuliginosa*, are active birds, moving restlessly when perched, with wings drooped and tail fanned. They are agile flyers, twisting and turning to catch insects on the wing. Two or three eggs are laid in the small neat nest built in a slender forked branch of a tree or shrub.

The sweet, chattering call of the Willie Wagtail, *Rhipidura leucophrys*, is often described as 'sweet pretty creature'. It is frequently to be heard at night, especially when the moon is bright. These bold, conspicuous little birds favour lightly timbered habitats and catch their insect prey in foliage, on the wing or while running along the ground. The nest is made of fine grass, bark and rootlets matted together with cobweb.

45

Like other babblers, White-browed Babblers, *Pomatostromus superciliosus*, are noisy, gregarious birds, which live in groups of up to about twelve. They are to be found in mallee, mulga and dry scrublands over the southern half of Australia. Several domed stick nests are built by the group, one to be used for nesting and the others for communal roosting. They are omniverous, often feeding on the ground or on tree trunks.

More likely to be heard than seen, the aptly-named Clamorous Reed Warbler, *Acrocephalus stentoreus*, breeds in summer, in reed beds and tall waterside vegetation. Here they usually remain hidden, but their loud sweet calls are frequently heard. The nest is a deep cup anchored to several vertical stems in dense cover. Most Reed Warblers migrate north during winter, though some birds do overwinter in the breeding areas, going unnoticed because they do not call at this time.

One of the best-known small birds of southeastern Australia, the Superb Blue Wren, *Malurus cyaneus*, is common wherever there is thick cover associated with clearings and open space. In family parties, they forage for insects by hopping jauntily over the ground with characteristically cocked tails, or moving quickly through undergrowth. Families consist of a dominant male, a breeding female, non-breeding adults of both sexes and first-year birds. The male in his brilliant blue breeding plumage is in strong contrast to the brown female. The female alone incubates the 3 to 4 eggs, which she lays in a domed nest. After the first brood leaves the nest, the female may build and lay again, leaving the non-breeding birds in the group to rear the first family.

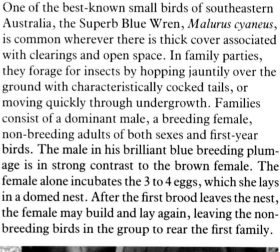

Rufous Bristle Birds, *Dasyornis broadbenti*, are shy, ground-dwelling birds occurring in dense scrub and rainforest undergrowth in coastal southeastern South Australia and western Victoria. Bristle Birds get their name from the stiff, curving bristles at the base of the bill. A domed nest with a side entrance is built close to the ground.

Thornbills are small, active brown birds, which forage in parties and small flocks. Several species often travel together, each utilising a different part of the habitat. Striated Thornbills, *Acanthiza lineata*, have brown eyes, white streaks on the crown and dark streaks on the face, throat and breast. They feed in the foliage and bark of trees and tall shrubs in dry forest and woodland. The neat nest with a hooded entrance is suspended in outer small branches of trees and shrubs.

Buff-rumped Thornbills, *Acanthiza reguloides*, have a pale eye. The buff-coloured rump contrasts with the olive-grey back, while the face and forehead are scalloped in buff. They forage on the ground amongst fallen debris and on lower tree branches in scrub, open forest and woodland. The domed nest may be on the ground, under bark or in a tree fork.

47

The large feet and claws of White-throated Treecreepers, *Cormobates leucophaea*, enable them to move easily up vertical tree trunks. Starting at the base and working in a spiral, they probe for insects with their long, curved bills in crevices in the bark. This female treecreeper brings prey to feed her young in the nest in a tree hole. The males do not have the orange cheek-spot.

The honeyeaters are a large group of birds characteristic of Australia. The Red Wattlebird, *Anthochaera carunculata*, in common with other honeyeaters, has a 'brush-tipped' tongue, adapted for gathering nectar and pollen. They are large, noisy and active birds inhabiting forests, woodlands and coastal scrubs across southern Australia. They are also called Gillbirds, because of their fleshy red neck wattles.

Easily identified by the black-bordered yellow stripe through the eye and its cheery call, the Yellow-faced Honeyeater, *Lichenostromus chrysops*, is found throughout eastern and southeastern Australia. The nest is a small cup of bark, grass and moss, camouflaged with lichens and suspended in the outer branches of a tree or shrub. In spring and summer, Yellow-faced Honeyeaters are usually seen alone or in pairs, but in autumn they move north in large flocks, returning in small flocks in late winter.

This White-eared Honeyeater, *Lichenostromus leucotis*, has built its cup-shaped nest amongst the protective foliage of an *Acacia* tree. These bold birds have been known to pull hair and fibre for their nests from the heads and clothing of bystanders. In southeastern Australia, they are to be found in various environments, from wet forest and woodland, to drier scrubs. In the southwest, however, only drier habitats such as mallee are used.

The Yellow-plumed Honeyeater, *Lichenostromus ornatus*, ranges from the mallee areas of central New South Wales, west through the Nullarbor, to the woodlands and forests of the south of Western Australia. It is distinguished by its bright yellow neck plume and its heavily streaked breast. Two eggs are laid in a nest of grass matted with plant down and cobweb, suspended in amongst the leaves of a mallee or a taller tree.

The white band on the nape, the dark chin and the red crescent of bare skin above the eye, are characteristic features of the White-naped Honeyeater, *Melithreptus lunatus*. The bird in this picture is feeding a young Pallid Cuckoo, *Cocomantis pallidus*, which it has raised as its own, following the laying of the egg in its nest by the parent cuckoos. This is called nest parasitism. White-naped Honeyeaters occur in woodlands and forests of eastern Australia and the humid southwestern part of Western Australia. Part of the eastern population migrates north in large flocks each autumn.

49

The Sydney district was still known as New Holland when in 1790 this bird was first identified and named. New Holland Honeyeaters, *Phylidonyris novaehollandiae*, which have white eyes, are boldly streaked black and white, with yellow on the wings and tail. They are noisy and conspicuous birds, which defend a group feeding territory as a flock, while pairs defend their own nesting territory.

The Tawny-crowned Honeyeater, *Phylidonyris melanops*, is typically found in low heaths, scrubs and mallee in southeastern and southwestern Australia. A shy bird, it may be hard to see, as it frequents low shrubs. However, it also perches in full view on vantage points such as dead branches or fences. Males have a song-flight in which they will fly up steeply from a perch, sing while hovering, then descend quickly. The nest is usually built among the stems of a low shrub or on the ground.

The chats are small birds belonging to a family unique to Australia. In common with other species in this group, the Crimson Chats, *Ephthianura tricolor*, have brightly coloured males and quietly coloured females. Male Crimson Chats have a crimson crown, throat and rump, while the females are brown with pale red on the breast and rump. They have characteristic undulating flight, showing the red or pink rump and the black tail with a white tip. Crimson Chats occur widely in the inland in salty areas, mallee, saltbush and spinifex, on hills and plains. They migrate north in autumn and south in spring, but are also nomadic, moving to areas where suitable rain has fallen. The deep cup nest is built low down in grass or in a low shrub.

The Orange Chat, *Ephthianura aurifrons*, is widely distributed in arid areas of central and western Australia. The male is distinguished by his orange forehead and breast, black face and throat and yellow rump. The female is much less brightly coloured and has no black on the face. Their preferred habitats are grassland, gibber, samphire and saltmarsh, where they feed in small groups on the ground or in low bushes. The nest is built close to the ground in a low shrub.

With his vivid black and white colouring, the male White-fronted Chat, *Ephthianura albifrons*, is unmistakable. The female is much greyer, with a pale breast band. The nest is a small cup built close to the ground in dense cover. Three or four spotted white eggs are laid. The parents share the care of the young and may distract intruders with a 'broken wing' act.

White-fronted Chats can be seen in pairs, small groups or large flocks. They favour low vegetation usually in damp habitats in saline estuarine and inland areas, swamp margins, shrubs and tussocks. They tend to be nomadic throughout their range in southern Australia, but are sedentary in coastal areas.

Any area where mistletoe grows is a suitable habitat for the Mistletoe Bird, *Dicaeum hirundaceum*. Even though the males are so brightly coloured, these tiny birds are difficult to see, as they feed amongst the outer leaves, flowers and mistletoe. They can be found wherever mistletoe is fruiting and are solitary except when they are breeding. Their tongues are adapted for nectar feeding, but their main diet consists of mistletoe fruits as well as other berries, insects and nectar. The fleshy outer layer of the mistletoe berries is digested quickly and the seeds excreted on to branches, where they germinate. The nest is a soft, pear-shaped bag with a side entrance, made of matted plant down and suspended from a twig. The young are fed first with insects and later with mistletoe berries.

Small, short-tailed birds with strong bills, Spotted Pardalotes, *Pardalotus punctatus*, are usually difficult to see, as they feed high in the upper foliage. They occur in the east, south and southwest of Australia, in forest, woodland, and scrublands. The nest is built in a chamber at the end of a tunnel in the soft soil of banks and road cuttings. The female, shown in this photograph, is duller than the male, which has bright yellow on the throat and under the tail, and white spots on the crown.

53

There are several races of Striated Pardalotes, *Pardalotus striatus*, occurring in suitable habitat over the Australian mainland and Tasmania. Also known by the name 'chip-chip', because of their sharp two-note call, they inhabit eucalypt forests and woodland, mulga, rainforest and mangroves. The nest is built in a tree hollow or in a chamber dug at the end of a tunnel in a bank.

The range of the Olive-backed Oriole, *Oriolus saggitatus*, extends across wooded areas in the northern and eastern mainland of Australia. These birds feed in the tops of trees, on insects, berries and other fruits and are nomadic or migratory, moving wherever supplies of insects and fruit are available. Orioles are not uncommon, but they are wary and the sound of their soft rolling call is likely to be the first sign of their presence.

The Red-browed Firetail, *Emblema temporalis*, builds a bulky nest of dry or green grass, with a tunnel entrance at one side. The male courts the female by approaching her holding a grass stem in his bill and bobbing up and down with his bill raised and his feathers fluffed. Red-browed Firetails feed mainly on seeds and insects. They are found in various habitats in eastern and southern Australia, where undergrowth and open spaces occur together.

White-browed Woodswallows, *Artamus superciliosus*, are beautifully coloured smoky grey and chestnut, with a white eyebrow and tail tip, the male being the more brightly coloured. The bloom on the plumage is due to the presence of powder down. This is produced by specialised feathers and helps maintain the feathers in good condition. Nests are often built in tree-forks, stump tops and hollow branches. Woodswallows occur over much of Australia, in numbers varying widely from pairs and small groups to mixed flocks of thousands, often associated with rainbow bee-eaters. They are nomadic and feed on insects in flight and, where blossom is abundant, on nectar, when they may associate with honeyeaters. They have a brush-tipped tongue adapted for nectar feeding.

The Dusky Woodswallow, *Artamus cyanopterus*, feeds on the wing on insects and on nectar when flowers are available. The sexes are alike in appearance. Both parents share the care of the young, which are reared in an untidy twig nest built under a piece of bark, in the top of a post, or in a broken tree limb. Dusky Woodswallows share with other woodswallows the habit of roosting in clusters, gathering in groups in a tree hollow or on a tree trunk.

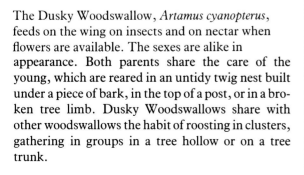

A male Australian Magpie-lark, *Grallina cyanoleuca*, brings food to his hungry brood. Females can be distinguished by their white face and throat, while immature birds have a white eyebrow and throat. These common birds are also called 'peewees'. from their characteristic call. They are to be found Australia-wide, typically in open areas near water. The mud nest is lined with grass, hair and feathers and is often built on a horizontal branch overhanging water.

Grey Butcherbirds, *Cracticus torquatus*, are so-called because of their habit of wedging and storing larger prey in forked branches or on thorns. They belong to a family of predatory birds which range through Australia and New Guinea. Their preferred habitats include forest margins, woodland, scrub and cleared land where they proclaim their territory with their beautiful call. They hunt for insects, small birds, reptiles and mammals, flying swiftly after their prey from a vantage point on a branch.

The early morning carolling of the Australian Magpie, *Gymnorhina tibicen*, is surely one of Australia's most beautiful and well-known bird calls. Magpies have benefited from changes to the environment made since European settlement, as they prefer habitats with a combination of trees and open areas. Successful breeding usually occurs where groups hold a permanent territory, with a dominant male, several breeding females and other non-breeding birds. Around nesting time some magpies may attack humans who approach too closely, by diving on them from behind.

Pied Currawongs, *Strepera graculina*, are large black birds, which like other currawongs have strong bills and yellow eyes. They are distinguished in flight by a crescent-shaped white patch on each wing and white at the base and tip of the tail. They occur in eastern Australia from Cape York to southwestern Victoria. They breed in forests in the ranges and foothills, moving to more open coastal lowlands in autumn.

The smallest of our five species of corvids (crows and ravens), the Little Raven, *Corvus mellori*, occurs in southeastern Australia in most habitats except closed forests. Adults have a white eye, while the eyes of immature birds are brown or hazel. They are gregarious birds and several pairs commonly nest close together or even in the same tree. Outside the breeding season, adults and young birds leave the breeding area in large flocks, wandering to wherever conditions are suitable.

57

Laughing Kookaburras, *Dacelo novaeguineae*, which are Australia's largest kingfishers, are famous for the 'laughing' call which gives them their name. Family groups, which consist of a mated pair with several of their offspring, advertise their territory by calling together, usually in the morning or evening. This display is often answered by other groups. Kookaburras feed on small animals such as lizards, frogs, mice, insects and other birds. They hunt by watching from a perch, then gliding down to pounce on their prey. Nesting takes place in a hollow, usually in a tree trunk or branch. The 2 to 4 white eggs are laid in debris at the bottom of the hole.

Jewel-coloured Sacred Kingfishers, *Halcyon sancta*, are found over most of Australia. They prefer forests and woodlands, usually not far from water, and the margins of lakes and rivers, mangroves and seashores. Their nests are made in tree hollows or holes in termite mounds and earth banks. Many of the Sacred Kingfishers which breed in southern Australia migrate north in autumn as far as New Guinea, while northern birds do not undertake such regular movements.

Barn Owls, *Tyto alba*, are so named because of their habit of roosting in barns, although they also roost in tree hollows, thick foliage, caves or on ledges. The Australian race of this almost worldwide species occurs all over Australia in woodland and forest, grassland, offshore islands and even in treeless areas such as the Nullarbor. The heart-shaped facial area aids detection of sound, and Barn Owls are able to locate prey by sound alone. They also have very acute vision and can see to hunt with very little light. They feed entirely on animals, particularly rodents.

Although the Tawny Frogmouth, *Podargus strigoides*, is a nocturnal bird, it is not an owl. Its call is a repeated soft 'oom oom oom'. Frogmouths range throughout Australia in timbered country and trees bordering open areas. They hunt silently at dusk and during the night. With their broad wide bills, they take insects or small vertebrates on the ground or on branches. By day, Frogmouths sit quite still, looking just like broken branches or stumps. The flimsy nest is a platform of sticks, placed in a fork in a large horizontal branch. Two white rounded eggs are laid.

Black Kites, *Milvus migrans*, are widespead soaring birds of prey, often seen in large flocks in northern and inland Australia. Their range is wide, including southern Europe, Africa, and Asia to New Guinea. They fly characteristically on bowed wings, constantly twisting their long forked tail. They are opportunist scavengers and flocks are often to be seen gathered around rubbish dumps and abattoirs.

The Australian Hobby, *Falco longipennis*, is a small falcon. A long-winged, swiftly-flying bird, it is an accomplished hunter, killing prey ranging from insects such as dragonflies to birds larger than itself. Although not common, it is to be found all over Australia. It favours wooded areas, but also uses other habitats from almost treeless plains to cities.

Swamp Harriers, *Circus aeruginosus*, are large hawks with long wings, tails and legs. They hunt by flying and gliding on upswept wings, low over swamps, crops and tall grass, and are often to be seen sitting upright on posts or on the ground. First-year birds are a uniform dark brown, while adults are more lightly-coloured, with streaked breasts and white rumps. The nest is a platform of sticks, reeds and other vegetation built in dense reeds, either in water or on the ground. Three to five eggs are laid and hatch in 33 days. The female incubates the eggs and feeds the chicks, while the male hunts.

The Australian Kestrel, *Falco cenchroides*, is a beautiful small hovering falcon. It is common in a wide variety of habitats, but prefers open woodlands and cultivated areas. Kestrels feed on grasshoppers and mice, but also take other small animals such as reptiles and the young of ground-nesting birds. The female, which has a chestnut tail with black barring, is larger than the male (pictured), which has a pale grey tail with a black subterminal band. Kestrels are regularly seen perched on telegraph poles and fenceposts, or hovering over paddocks searching the ground for prey.

The Wedge-tailed Eagle, *Aquila audax*, is Australia's largest bird of prey, fully-grown birds having a wingspan of 2.5 metres. Like most birds of prey, the female eagles are larger than the males. Ranging Australia-wide in most habitats, even to treeless plains, they may be recognised in flight by the diamond-shaped tail and upswept wings.

The nest is a very large structure built of sticks and lined with green leaves. It is usually placed in a tree, at a height ranging from less than 2 metres to 30 metres above the ground, and is added-to over the years. A clutch of two eggs is usually laid, and often, though not always, the smaller chick will not survive. Wedge-tailed Eagles feed mainly on rabbits and the carcasses of road-killed animals such as kangaroos.

INDEX